Are you getting _all_ your library offers you? ---

   IN

     Books

     Magazines

     Newspapers

     Pamphlets

     Government Documents

     Pictures

     Maps

     Phonograph Records

     Sheet Music

     Story Hours

     Information Service

PUBLIC
LIBRARY
SYSTEM
MILWAUKEE

SONGS OF THE DREAM PEOPLE

SONGS OF THE

CHANTS AND IMAGES FROM THE INDIANS
AND ESKIMOS OF NORTH AMERICA

A Margaret K. McElderry Book

DREAM PEOPLE

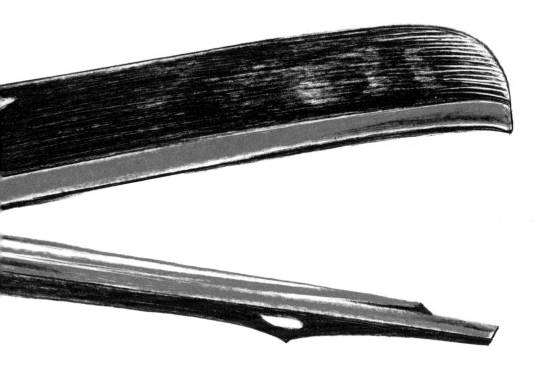

Edited and illustrated by

JAMES HOUSTON

ATHENEUM 1972 NEW YORK

By the same author

FOR YOUNG READERS

Akavak

Eagle Mask

Ghost Paddle

Tikta'liktak

The White Archer

Wolf Run

FOR ADULTS

Eskimo Prints

Ojibway Summer

The White Dawn *(a novel)*

ZUNI POT MOTIF (Binding)
MOHAVE DOLL SINGER (False title page)
KWAKIUTL CANNIBAL MASK (Title page)
BLACKFOOT QUILL DESIGN (Dedication page)

*This book is dedicated to
the first people of North America
with deep respect for their inspired past
and renewed hope for their future.*

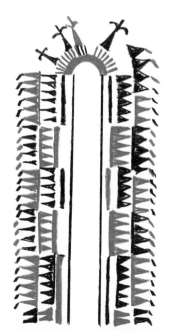

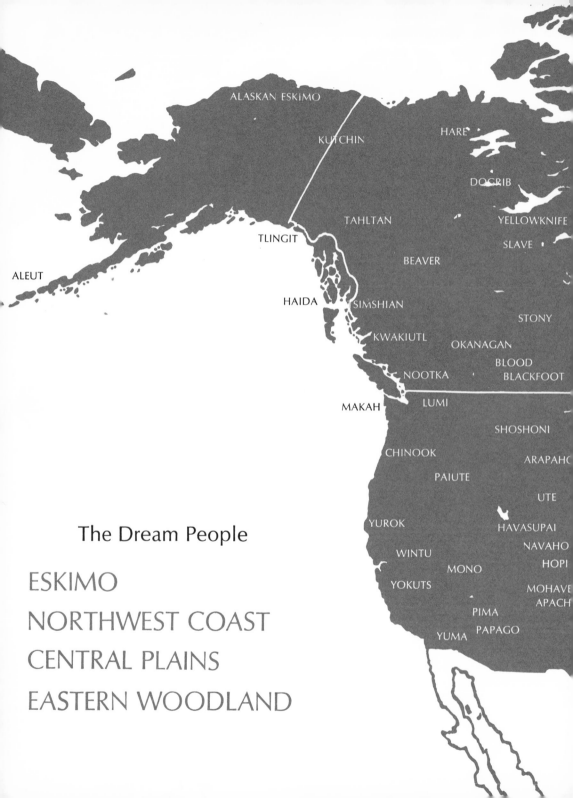

The Dream People

ESKIMO
NORTHWEST COAST
CENTRAL PLAINS
EASTERN WOODLAND

FOREWORD

The songs of the Indians and Eskimos are often set to the stroke of a paddle, to the flight of birds, to the rhythm of a running horse, or the thump of the corn grinding stone. These songs have a rich vitality about them, voicing with passion an endless search for the magic in life. Their song phrases are short and to the point, but some of the songs last a whole night, relying on their hypnotic repetitions to entrance the singer and his listeners and carry them to the doorposts of the other world.

For some, the other world is hidden in the sky, or under the earth, or in the mountains, or beneath the sea. All of the tribes agree that there is another world to which one may fly in death, in trances, or in dreams.

PUEBLO INDIAN BASKET FIGURE

Dreams are of great significance to both the Indians and Eskimos. Dreams have always been carefully interpreted by almost all the tribes, for they are thought to be messages from the other world that can foretell the future. To the Oglala Sioux the dream elk has overtones of sex, as does the white bear dream to the Eskimos of the Eastern Arctic.

Many of their songs we will never understand because both the Indians and Eskimos sometimes employ secret terms whose meanings are purposely hidden. The Plains people sometimes sang of horsetails when they meant scalps. The Eskimos sing of hunting maggots and lice when they really mean walrus and seals, for they fear that to use the real names of these sea beasts may offend them or the ghosts of those already dead.

As a part of the singing, a hunter or a warrior or a tribal priest might re-enact his triumphs or his failures. This often led to the creation of masks, carvings, paintings, and elaborate costumes to heighten the drama. Some of the clans of the Northwest Coast were so serious about their dance rituals that any slight mistake would destroy the entire ceremony for them, and the guilty dancer was sometimes put to death.

Within the Eastern Woodland tribes, chiefs were sometimes chosen because of their ability to deliver orations with great gestures and eloquence. These sachems had the strongest feelings for the use of similes and metaphors. For example, an Iroquois ambassador sent to the French governor at Quebec said to him, "Onontio, thou hast dispersed the clouds, the air is serene, the sky shows clearly, the sun is bright. I see no more trouble. Peace has made everything calm. My heart is at rest, I go away very happy."

Eskimo songs sometimes modulate from major to minor, which is extremely rare in primitive music and scarcely known in North American Indian songs. These songs of the Arctic coast generally proceed on an upward curve and end at about the same level as their beginning. Many Indian songs begin on a high note and descend, ending on the lowest note.

Traditionally the Indian and Eskimo people of America did not use word-rhymings in their songs and chants.

Indian and Eskimo objects may lie buried for centuries, but they often reappear, looking more beautiful than before. Un-recorded songs and dances, however, are man's most perishable intellectual possessions, for once lost they have no way of returning.

Here, recorded by a few, are some of the rare sounds of America's past, the philosophies of a wide variety of tribes that spanned a whole continent.

James Houston

o - ka kap-ce ka-na-a kap-ce-e ma-na-a qı-ma-yłu-yo - o tı-kı-yaŋ-mun   tı-

kıny-ay-naq-pu-cı - - ı um- ıaq-pan-nı-i qa-a-a-na o ke-ya- me-tät-qa-vuŋ-aı

u-va-ma-le u-va-ma-le mä-lɪk-caq-tuŋ-aı   ı o-ke-ya-lu- ŋa pı-ma-a-cu-

ne — aı yaŋ-a ya-ma ye   aı yaŋ-a ye

ESKIMO SONG

ESKIMO DRUM DANCE

IROQUOIS FALSE FACE MASK

EASTERN

We will watch the Northern Lights
playing their game of ball
in the cold, glistening country.
Then we will sit in beauty on the mountain
and watch the small stars
in their sleepless flight.

Abanaki

A ring of silver foxes,
a mist of silver foxes,
come and sit around the hunting moon.

Abanaki

ABANAKI PAINTED SKIN

WOODLAND

It is I who wear the morning star
on my forehead. . . .
All that grows upon the earth
is mine.

Iroquois

I hear the eagle bird
with his great feathers spread,
pulling the blanket back from the east.
How swiftly he flies,
bearing the sun to the morning.

Iroquois

IROQUOIS CORN POUNDER

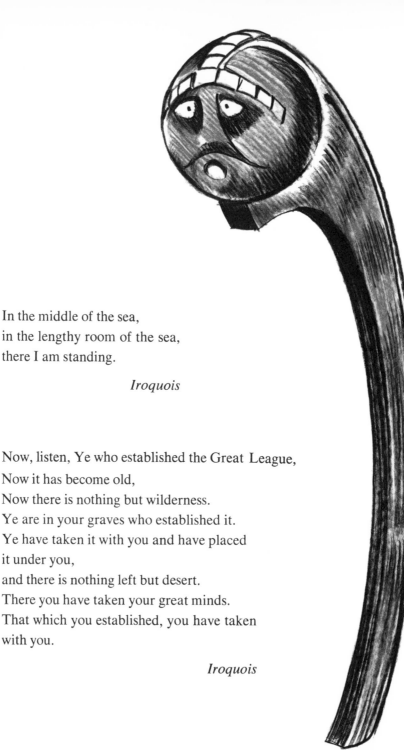

In the middle of the sea,
in the lengthy room of the sea,
there I am standing.

Iroquois

Now, listen, Ye who established the Great League,
Now it has become old,
Now there is nothing but wilderness.
Ye are in your graves who established it.
Ye have taken it with you and have placed
it under you,
and there is nothing left but desert.
There you have taken your great minds.
That which you established, you have taken
with you.

Iroquois

IROQUOIS WAR CLUB

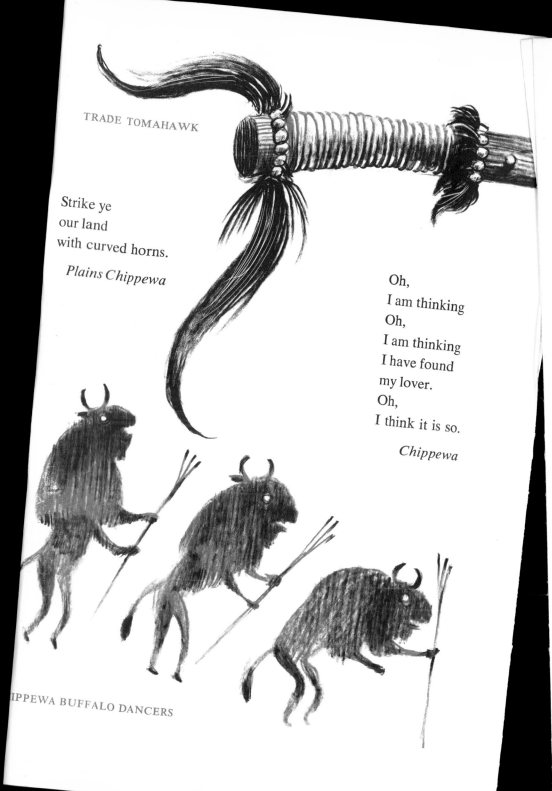

TRADE TOMAHAWK

Strike ye
our land
with curved horns.

Plains Chippewa

Oh,
 I am thinking
Oh,
 I am thinking
 I have found
my lover.
Oh,
 I think it is so.

Chippewa

CHIPPEWA BUFFALO DANCERS

OJIBWA PICTOGRAPH

Over the sea, the frozen sea,
They went to enjoy it.
On the wonderful slippery water,
on the stone-hard water all went,
on the great tidal sea, the muscle-bearing
sea.

Delaware

Hear my voice, Birds of War!
I prepare a feast for you to feed on;
I see you cross the enemy's lines.
Like you I shall go.
I wish the swiftness of your wings;
I wish the vengeance of your claws;
I muster my friends;
I follow your flight.
Ho, you young men warriors,
Bear your angers to the place of fighting!
Here on my breast have I bled!
See—see! these are fighting-scars!
Mountains tremble at my yell!
I strike for life.

Ojibwa

DEER MASK, DELAWARE

The red streams of my veins run
toward you,
as forest streams to the sun in the moon
of bright nights.
When you are beside me my heart sings,
dancing before the Wind-spirit
in the moon of strawberries.

Ojibwa

Drifting snow,
why do I sing?
Ojibwa

The spirit walking in the sky
takes care of us.

Ojibwa

BEAVERTAIL BAG,
OJIBWA

A loon I thought it was,
But it was
My love's splashing oar.

Chippewa

The
only
I am

The noise of passi
On the prairie—
Is it men or gods
Who come out of

Plains

CHIPPEWA PICTOGRAPH

The Sioux women
pass to and fro wailing
as they gather up
their wounded men.
The voice of their weeping comes back
to us.

Plains Chippewa

I
of the owl
am afraid
whenever I am sitting alone
in the wigwam.

Chippewa

CENTRAL 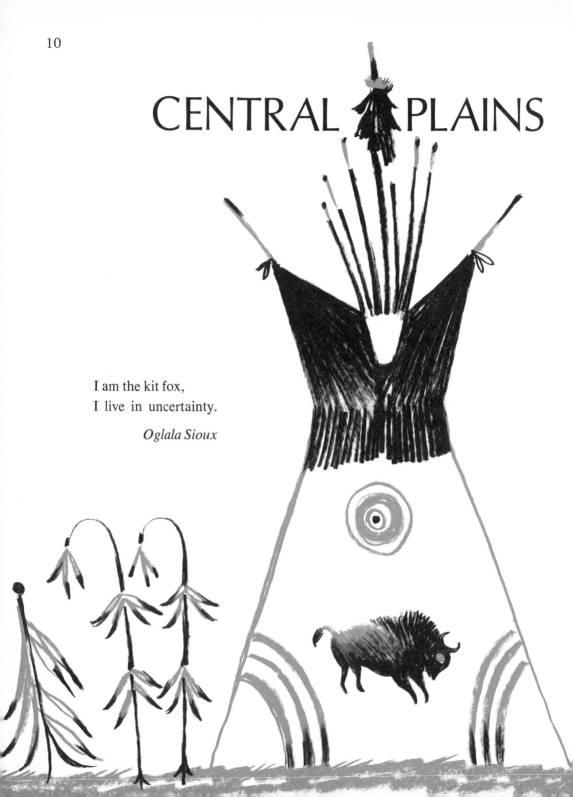 PLAINS

I am the kit fox,
I live in uncertainty.

Oglala Sioux

Out of the earth, I sing for them.
A horse nation, I sing for them.
Out of the earth, I sing for them.
The animals, I sing for them.

Teton Sioux

SIOUX HORSEMAN AND TENT

At night may I roam
When the owl is hooting.
At dawn may I roam
When the crow is calling.
Then may I roam.

Teton Sioux

A warrior I have been.
Now it is all over,
A hard time I have.

Sioux

SIOUX DANCER

The whole world is coming,
A nation is coming, a nation is coming,
the eagle has brought the message to the
tribe.
Over the whole earth they are coming;
the buffalo are coming, the buffalo are
coming,
the Crow has brought the message to the
tribe.

Sioux

If you are lazy or a coward,
You will sleep with the coyotes.
You should not cut your woman's nose.
No woman will give her flesh for you.
The buffalo will laugh at you,
If you tell lies.

Oglala Sioux

It shall be
that I rejoice,
O my son.
Your elder brother
you have brought back,
O my son.
It shall be
that I rejoice,
O my son.

Sioux

SIOUX HORSEMAN

I sought a vision and the Bear God spoke to me:
"The young man should have the horsetails waved over him;
He will provide for his women and children;
He will be brave and truthful and people will listen to him;
He will have plenty and give freely."

Oglala Sioux

I bring the whirlwind
that you may know one another.
We shall live again.
We shall live again!

Cheyenne

SCALP CEREMONY

Come on, Caddo, we are all going up,
Come on, Caddo, we are all going up
To the great village—He'e'ye'!
To the great village—He'e'ye'!
With our Father above,
With our Father above, where he dwells
on high—He'e'ye'!
Where our Mother dwells—He'e'ye'!
Where our Mother dwells—He'e'ye'!

Caddo

SIOUX DREAM FIGURE

The wind stirs the willows.
The wind stirs the grasses.
A slender antelope,
A slender antelope,
he is wallowing upon the ground.
Whirlwind! Whirlwind!
The snowy earth comes gliding, the snowy
earth come gliding.
The rocks are ringing,
The rocks are ringing,
They are ringing in the mountains.

Paiute

16

Because I am poor,
I pray for every living creature.

Kiowa

The Father will descend.
Everybody will arise.
Stretch out your hands.
The earth will tremble.

Kiowa

My words are tied in one
With the great mountains,
With the great rocks,
I, one with my body
and my heart.

Yokuts

KIOWA SINGERS

There came a gray owl at sunset,
there came a gray owl at sunset,
hooting softly around me.
He brought terror to my heart.

Southwest Tribes

A hat of eagle feathers,
a hat of eagle feathers,
a headdress was made for me
that made my heart grow stronger.

Southwest Tribes

The songs commence at nightfall,
and the winds blow toward the north.
The winds are blowing strongly,
blowing my tail toward the north.
See the small dogs come running;
see the poor dogs come running.
See the horsemen coming after;
see the horsemen come laughing.

Southwest Tribes

SOUTHWEST HORSEMAN

Throughout the world
Who is there like me?
Who is like me?
I touch the sky,
Indeed I touch the sky!

Winnebago

Ho! Ye Sun, Moon, Stars, all ye that
move in the heavens,
I bid you hear me!
Into your midst has come a new life.
Consent ye, I implore!
Make its path smooth that it may reach
the brow of the first hill!

Omaha

PLAINS CHIEF WITH PEACE PIPE

The deer is taking away the daylight.
After taking away the daylight,
he named it Darkness.

Yaqui

In summer the rains come,
The grass grows up,
and the deer has new horns.

Yaqui

DEER MAN MASK,
OKLAHOMA

The water bug
is drawing the shadows of evening
toward him across the water.

Yuma

The owl hooted,
Telling of the morning star.
He hooted again,
Announcing the dawn.

Yuma

OWL, STONE MORTAR,
SOUTHWEST COAST

EAGLE MAN,
SOUTHERN CULT COMPLEX

By what name is thy bride known?
Is she beautiful?
Are her eyes soft as the light of the moon?
Is she a strong woman?
Didst thou understand her signs as she danced to thee?
I know not whether thou lovest her, Tiakens.
What saidst the old man, her father,
when you asked for his pretty daughter?
What betrothal gifts didst thou give her?

Tenasa

This is the White Land; we arrive singing,
headdresses waving in the breeze.
We have come! We have come!
The land trembles with our dancing and
singing.

Yoku

YOKU DANCER

I have made a footprint,
Smoke arises from my house.
I have made a footprint,
There is cheer in my house.
I have made a footprint,
I live in the light of day.

Osage

I rise. I rise.
I whose tread makes the earth tremble,
In whose thighs there is strength,
I who whips his back with his tail when in rage,
In whose humped shoulders there is power,
I who shakes his mane when angered,
I whose horns are sharp and curved.

Osage

A wolf
I considered myself
but
the owls are hooting
and
the night I fear.

Osage

OSAGE DECORATED BUFFALO SKULL

I am a wanderer,
I shall die stretched out.

Lamba

I am like a bear.
I hold up my hands
waiting for the sun to rise.

Northern Ute

SOUTHWEST WALL PAINTING

Sun, my relative,
Be good coming out,
Do something good for us.

Havasupai

My children, my children,
Look! The earth is about to move
Look! The earth is about to move.
My father told me so.
My father told me so.

Arapaho

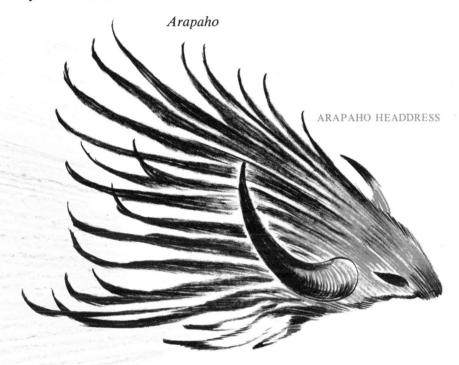

ARAPAHO HEADDRESS

Father, the Morning Star!
Father, the Morning Star!
Look on us, we have danced until daylight,
Take pity on us—Hi'i'i!

Arapaho

26

My dear friend,
your husband,
at me
how he stared.
Will you throw him away?

Mandan and Hidatsa

T-cho, the Sun, said,
"You are my children,
I am your mother,
I will make light.
I will shine for you."

Yuchi

MANDAN MOTHER

On the stone ridge east I go,
On the white road crouching I go,
I, Han, whistle on the road of stars.
The circuit of earth, which you see,
The scattering of stars in the sky, which you see,
All that is the place for my hair.

Wintu

SIA SUNFLOWER MOTIF

Come you, that all trees and seeds may
come up and be strong.
Come you hither; all come.

Sia

Let our children live and be happy.
Send us the good south winds.
Send us your breath over the lakes that
our great world may be made beautiful
and our people may live.
There, far off, my Sun Father arises, as-
cends the ladder, comes forth from his place.
May all complete the road of life, may all
grow old.
May the children inhale more of the sacred
breath of life.
May all my children have corn that they
may complete the road of life.
Here sit down; here remain; we give you
our best thoughts.
Hasten over the meal road; we are jealous
of you.
We inhale the sacred breath through our
prayer plumes.

Sia

SOUTHWEST CLIFF DRAWINGS

White floating clouds,
Clouds like the plains,
Come and water the earth.
Sun embrace the earth
that she may be fruitful.
Moon, lion of the north,
Bear of the west,
Badger of the south,
Wolf of the east,
Eagle of the heavens,
Shrew of the earth,
Elder war hero,
Warriors of the six mountains of the
world,
Intercede with the cloud people for us
That they may water the earth.

Sia

SIA POT

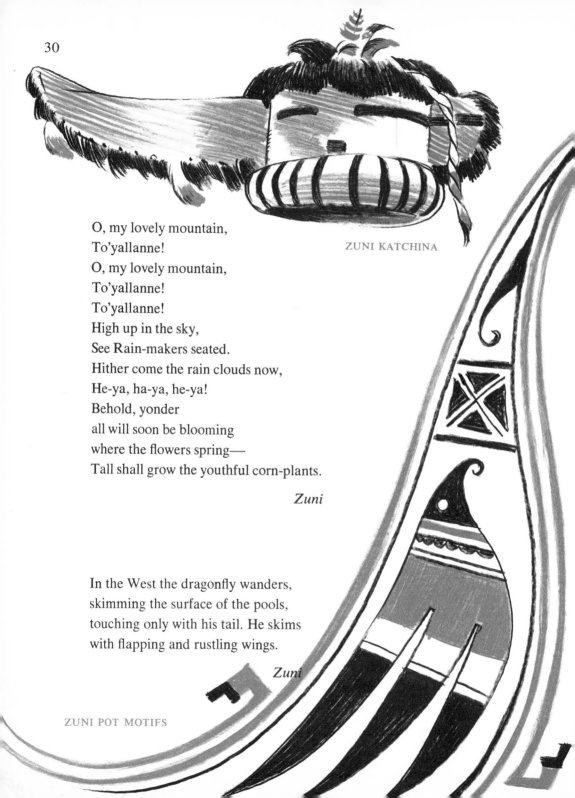

ZUNI KATCHINA

O, my lovely mountain,
To'yallanne!
O, my lovely mountain,
To'yallanne!
To'yallanne!
High up in the sky,
See Rain-makers seated.
Hither come the rain clouds now,
He-ya, ha-ya, he-ya!
Behold, yonder
all will soon be blooming
where the flowers spring—
Tall shall grow the youthful corn-plants.

Zuni

In the West the dragonfly wanders,
skimming the surface of the pools,
touching only with his tail. He skims
with flapping and rustling wings.

Zuni

ZUNI POT MOTIFS

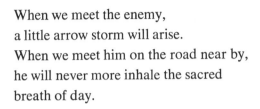

When we meet the enemy,
a little arrow storm will arise.
When we meet him on the road near by,
he will never more inhale the sacred
breath of day.

Zuni

You talk about and fear me;
you talk about and fear me;
As, like the sinuous snake,
I go upon the water.
Younger brother, I am Beaver,
I am the quick-eared Beaver
that gnaws the trees of the forest.
'Tis I who overthrow them.

Zuni

Child of the Raven! Child of the Raven!
You of the dazzling power!
See my magic power shining like the
mirage.

Zuni

ZUNI FETISH

The poor little bee
That lives in the tree
Has only one arrow
in his quiver.

Kaniga

Holy visions!
Hither come, we pray you, come unto us,
bringing with you joy;
come, oh, come to us, holy visions,
bringing with you joy.
Holy visions!
Now they touch the children, gently touch them,
giving dreams of joy;
gently touch each one—holy visions—
giving dreams of joy.

Pawnee

BEE BASKET MOTIF

Give heed, my child, lift your eyes, behold
the one who has brought you life.
Behold, my child. Life you have received
and finished is the task.
Give heed, my child. Look. Red paint
leaves the vigor of life with you.

Pawnee

It is there that our hearts are set,
In the expanse of the heavens.

Pawnee

As I lay sleeping, as I lay dreaming,
Out of the distance came one advancing,
one whom I ne'er had seen before, but
when her voice addressed me, straight-
way I knew her—
Lo! 'Twas our Mother, she whom we
know.

Pawnee

PAWNEE WOMAN'S SHIRT

Look, where they come, see them, see them,
young ones and old ones!
Look! Here they come, this way, that way,
flocking together.
Hither they come, shouting like eagles,
shouting come.
Joyous, happy, gladly come they, gaily
coming, coming hither.
See where they come, flocking like birds,
shouting like eagles,
as they come to the Fathers.

Pawnee

PAWNEE DANCE DRAWING

For winter:

> In winter time
> If the old Indians' faces are hot,
> That is a sign that there is to be snow.
> When in the spring
> The water rises,
> It is going to be very cold.
> When the thaw is coming,
> You feel aching and cramping all over;
> You see the northern light if the thaw is to last.
> If it is going to be windy,
> The ears hm, hum, hm. . . .

Blood

Summer time:

> If it is going to be dry,
> Stars do not shine;
> They are far, far off,
> And the springs are dry.
> If it is going to be wet,
> The stars shine;
> The sun has a kind of damp heat
> If it is going to be a rainy summer.
> The springs open where it was dry.
> And there is always cold wind from the northeast.
> If it is to be a hard winter,
> All the wild animals get fat.

Blood

The Morning Star is like a man; he is painted red all over; that is the color of life. He is clad in leggings and a robe is wrapped about him. On his head is a soft downy eagle's feather, painted red. This feather represents the soft, light cloud that is high in the heavens, and the red is the touch of a ray of the coming sun. The soft, downy feather is the symbol of breath and life. This is a very sacred song.

Oh, Morning Star, for thee we watch!
Dimly comes thy light from distant skies.
We see thee, then lost thou art.
Morning Star, thou bringest life to us.

Oh, Morning Star, thy form we see!
Clad in shining garments dost thou come,
Thy plume touched with rosy light.
Morning Star, thou now art vanishing.

Pawnee

PAWNEE DRAWING

Now I walk with Talking God.
With goodness and beauty in all things around me I go;
With goodness and beauty I follow immortality.
Thus, being I, I go.

Navaho

My great corn plants,
Among them I walk,
I speak to them,
They hold out their hands to me.

Navaho

NAVAHO SAND PAINTING

Farewell, my younger brother!
From the holy places the gods come for me.
You will never see me again; but when the
showers pass and the thunders peal,
"There," you will say, "is the voice of my
elder brother."
And when the harvest comes, of the beautiful
birds and grasshoppers you will say,
"There is the ordering of my elder
brother!"

NAVAHO SKIN MASK

Navaho

In Tsegihi,
in the house made of dawn,
in the house made of evening twilight,
in the house made of dark cloud,
in the house made of rain and mist, of pollen,
of grasshoppers,
where the dark mist curtains the doorway,
the path to which is on the rainbow,
where the zigzag lightning stands high on
top,
where the he-rain stands high on top,
Oh, male divinity!

Navaho

NAVAHO FETISH

To the abode of the deer I came up.
To the doorpost of darkness I came up.
To the doorpost of daylight I came up.
To the doorpost of moon I came up.
To the doorpost of sun I came up.

Navaho

Powerless! Powerless!
Powerless is my magic crystal!
Powerless! Powerless!
I shall become as stone.

CLOUD SYMBOL

Pima

From the mountain's summit
Down the trail, coming now,
Comes the deer to my singing.

Navaho

NAVAHO SILVER SYMBOL

Hi-ihiya naiho-o! Pluck out the feathers
from the wing of the Eagle and turn them
toward the east where lie the large clouds.
Hitciya yahina-a! Pluck out the soft down
from the breast of the Eagle and turn it
toward the west where sail the small clouds.

Navaho

EAGLE SYMBOL

The sun is slowly departing,
It is slower in its setting;
Black bats will be swooping when the sun
is gone,
That is all.

Papago

SOUTHWEST
HORSE DRAWING

Black hair rope is what you used in roping me.
You treated me badly.
You even threw me down and tied me.
Not satisfied with that, you tied a knot in
my tail.
That made me disgusted.

Navaho

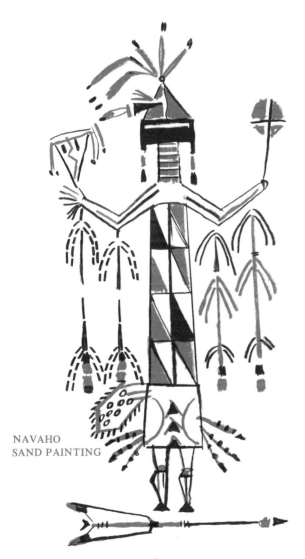

NAVAHO
SAND PAINTING

Far as man can see,
comes the rain,
comes the rain with me.
From the Rain-Mount,
Rain-Mount far away,
comes the rain,
comes the rain with me.
O'er the corn,
O'er the corn, tall corn,
comes the rain,
comes the rain with me.
'Mid the Lightnings,
'Mid the lightnings' zigzag,
'Mid the lightnings' flashing,
comes the rain,
comes the rain with me.
'Mid the swallows,
'Mid the swallows blue,
Chirping glad together,
comes the rain,
comes the rain with me.
Through the pollen,
Through the pollen blest,
All in pollen hidden,
comes the rain,
comes the rain with me.
Far as man can see,
comes the rain,
comes the rain with me.

Navaho

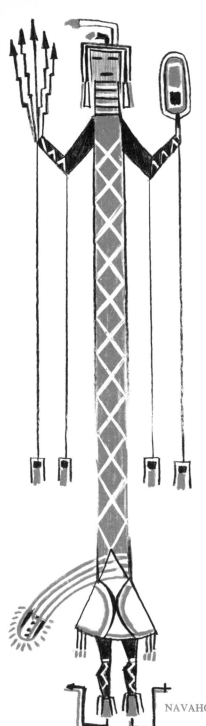

The voice of thunder
Within the dark cloud,
Again and again it sounds,
The voice that beautifies the land.

Navaho

SOUTHWEST BIRD SYMBOL

The Magpie! The Magpie! Here underneath
in the white of his wings are the footsteps
of morning.
It dawns! It dawns!

Navaho

NAVAHO SAND PAINTING OF THUNDER

Weave us a garment of brightness
That we may walk fittingly where birds sing,
That we may walk fittingly where grass is green,
Oh, our mother the earth,
Oh, our father the sky.

Tewa

NAVAHO JEWELRY

In the great night my heart will go out;
Toward me the darkness comes rustling.
In the great night my heart will go out.

Apache

APACHE DANCERS

A poor man takes the songs in his hand
and drops them near the place where the
sun sets.
See, Cowaka, run to them and take them in
your hand
and place them under the sunset.

Apache

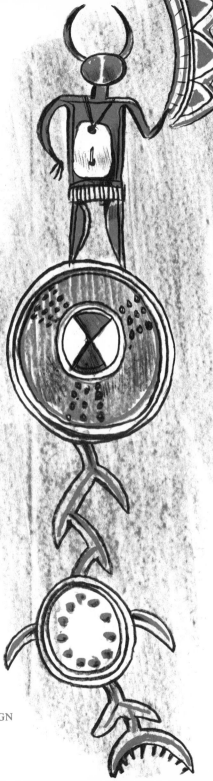

A cloud on top of Evergreen Mountain is
singing,
A cloud on top of Evergreen Mountain is
standing still.
It is raining and thundering up there,
It is raining here.
Under the mountain the corn tassels are
shaking,
Under the mountain the slender spikes of
child corn are glistening.

Apache

APACHE SHIRT DESIGN

The sunbeams stream forward,
dawn boys with moccasins shimmering yellow.
The rainbow moves forward—
dawn maidens, with shirts of yellow,
dance over us. Beautifully it is dawning.

Mescalero Apache

APACHE DRUM CEREMONY

Blue evening falls,
Blue evening falls.
Nearby in every direction
It sets the corn tassels trembling.

Papago

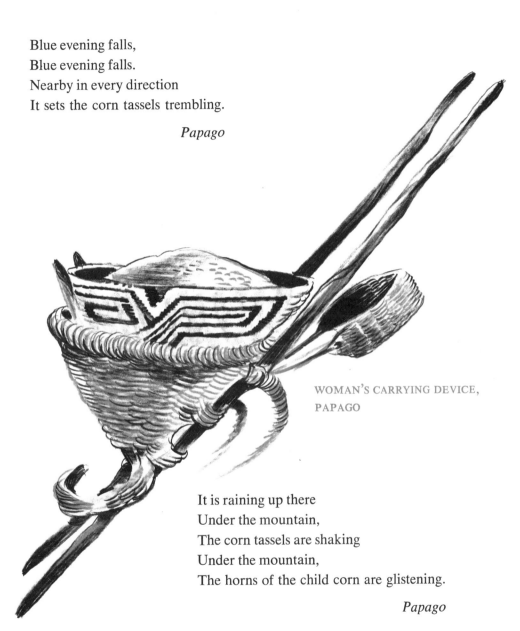

WOMAN'S CARRYING DEVICE,
PAPAGO

It is raining up there
Under the mountain,
The corn tassels are shaking
Under the mountain,
The horns of the child corn are glistening.

Papago

The sun's rays
lie along the eagle's wings
and stretch beyond their tips.

Papago

NECKLACE,
EAGLE CLAWS

Where am I running from
that I come here?
Am I a crazy woman
with a painted face?

Papago

A low range of mountains,
Toward them I'm running.
From the top of these mountains
I shall see the dawn.

Papago

By the sandy water I breathe in the odor of
the sea;
From there the wind comes and blows over
the world.
By the sandy water I breathe in the odor
of the sea;
From there the clouds come and rain falls
over the world.

Papago

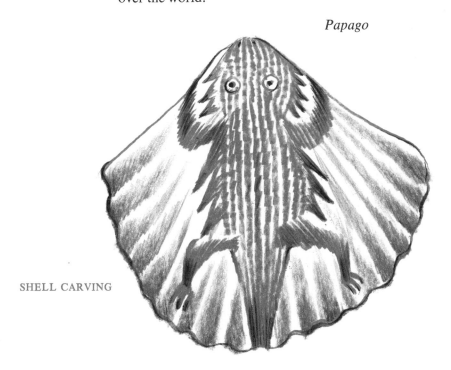

SHELL CARVING

I have made the sun!
I have made the sun!
Hurling it high
In four directions.
To the east I threw it
to run its appointed course.

Pima

PIMA BASKET

The bright dawn appears in the heavens;
The bright dawn appears in the heavens,
And the paling Pleiades grow dim,
The moon is lost in the rising sun.

Pima

SOUTHWEST SYMBOL,
WINDSTORM SERPENT

Wind now commences to sing;
Wind now commences to sing.
The land stretches before me,
Before me stretches away.

Wind's house now is thundering;
Wind's house now is thundering.
I go roaring over the land,
The land covered with thunder.

The Black Snake Wind came to me,
The Black Snake Wind came to me,
Came and wrapped itself around me,
Came here running with its songs.

Pima

NOOTKA
KILLER WHALE

My little son,
you will put a whale harpoon
and a sealing spear into your canoe,
not knowing what use you will make of them.

Makah

Sing your song
Looking up at the sky.

Nootka

NORTHWEST COAST

You whose day it is
make it beautiful.
Get out your rainbow,
make it beautiful.

Nootka

NOOTKA WOVEN HAT

Even from war, people get away,
but not from you, Raven woman.

Kwakiutl

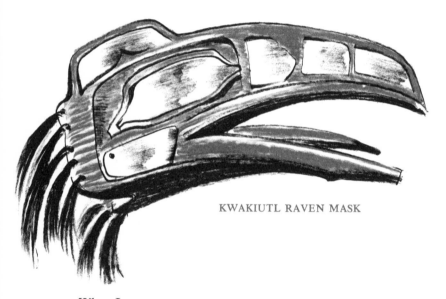

KWAKIUTL RAVEN MASK

When I am a man,
I shall be a hunter, O father,
I shall be a harpooner, O father,
I shall be a canoe-builder, O father,
I shall be an artisan, O father,
Then we shall not be in want, O father.
Ya, ha, ha, ha.

Kwakiutl

What of olden times,
shall I tell you of olden times?
What of olden times
my grandchildren?
You of olden times,
you of olden times,
a cloud,
lay on the mountains.

Kwakiutl

COPPER COIN

Be ready, oh, chiefs' sons of the tribes.
I come to make my husband a great chief.
I, mistress of chiefs and princes,
I am seated on many coppers,
I have many names and privileges,
I have many masks and dishes.
Now the marriage feast.
Who shall be my husband?

Kwakiutl

How shall we hide from the bear that is moving
  all around the world?
Let us cover our backs
  with dirt that the terrible great bear from
  the north of the world may not find us.

Kwakiutl

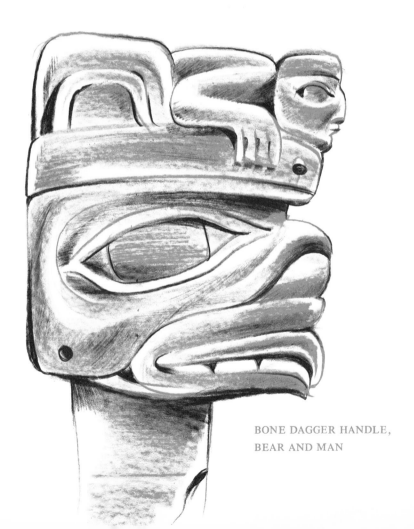

BONE DAGGER HANDLE,
BEAR AND MAN

Skyspear,
rising, rising.
Crests of Raven, Bear, and Fireweed,
rising, rising.

Tsimshian

Hold in your breath, Chief,
that it may be calm.

Tsimshian

Nexnox, Nexnox!
Chief, Chief!
Have a pity upon us!
Look down and see
what those under you,
whom you made, are doing!
Pull up your foot
and sweep off your face!

Tsimshian

TOTEM POLE,
NORTHWEST COAST

We are also going to be invited
to Killisnoo.
High-caste people
are going to eat.

Haida

If one had control of death
it would be very easy
to die with a Wolf woman.
It would be very pleasant.

Haida

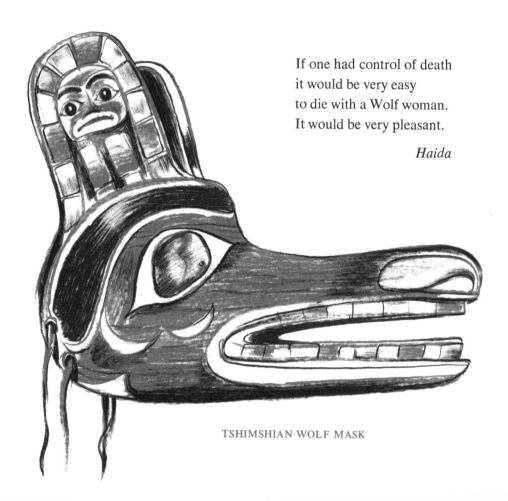

TSHIMSHIAN WOLF MASK

HAIDA HUMAN MASK

Behind Sea-Lion Town
I was looking around a while;
the future chief I found,
just big enough to walk.
Take care, take care, my own chief!
Take care, my own master!

Women are better than men,
women are better than men.
Women have more property.
Chiefs of my family,
where are you?

Haida

I have taken the woman of beauty
for my wife;
I have taken her from her friends.
I hope her kinsmen will not come
and take her away from me.
I will be kind to her.
Berries, berries I will give her from the
hill
and roots from the ground.
I will do everything to please her.
For her I made this song and for her I
sing it.

Haida

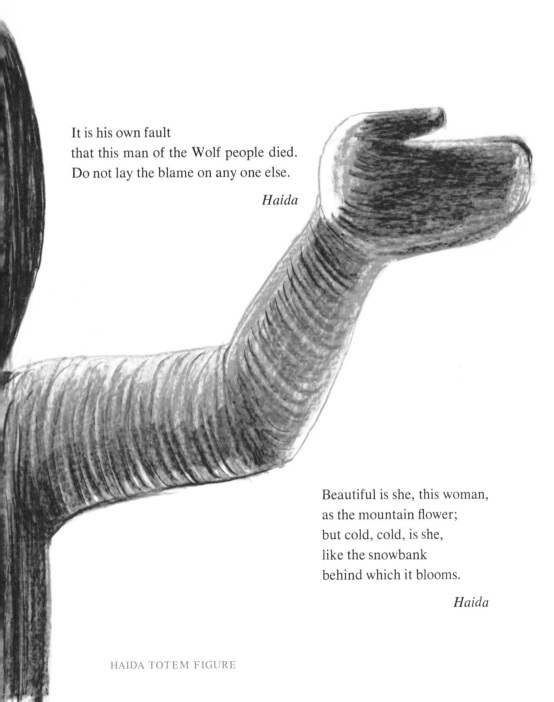

It is his own fault
that this man of the Wolf people died.
Do not lay the blame on any one else.

Haida

Beautiful is she, this woman,
as the mountain flower;
but cold, cold, is she,
like the snowbank
behind which it blooms.

Haida

HAIDA TOTEM FIGURE

It is not now as it was in olden times.
Even slaves are beginning to own good
abalone shells!

Haida

HAIDA CANOE

Perhaps you expect to sit up high in your father's canoe,
chief-woman, and look around upon all things.
Be careful, chief-woman!

Perhaps you expect to sit up high in your father's canoe,
chief-woman, and look around the place
whence abalones come.
Be careful, chief-woman.
A child of noble family sits quietly.

Haida

Let me shoot a small bird
for my younger brother,
Let me spear a small trout
for my sister.

Tlingit

TLINGIT HELMET

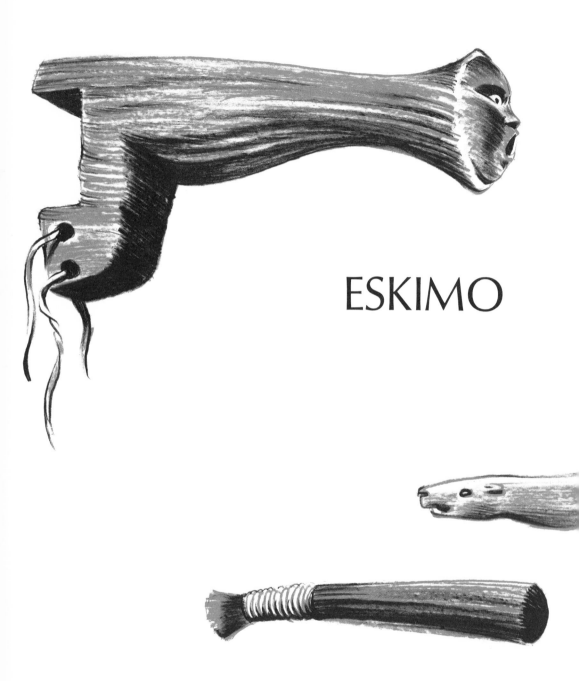

ESKIMO

Glorious it is
To see long-haired winter caribou
Returning to the forests,
While the herd follows the ebb-mark of the sea
With a storm of clattering hooves.
Glorious it is
When wandering time is come.

Alaskan Eskimo

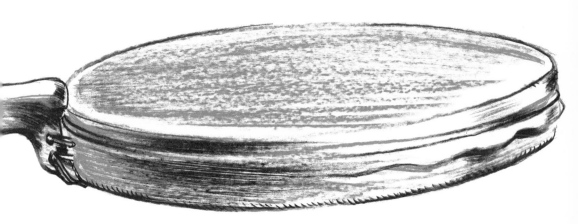

SKIN DRUM AND HANDLES

Ayii, Ayii, Ayii, Ayii,
Wondering I saw them,
Great black beasts,
Running, standing,
Eating flowers on the high plain.
On my belly I crept to them
With my bow and arrows in my mouth.
The big one reared up in surprise
As my arrow quivered in his chest.
The herd scattered,
Running on the high plain,
And I, small I, sat singing
By the big bull's side.
Ayii, Ayii.

Central Eskimo

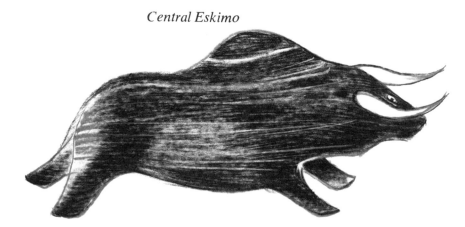

STONE MUSK-OX

STONE CARVING OF MAN

I want to laugh, I, because my sledge it is broken.
Because its ribs are broken I want to laugh.
Here at Talaviuyaq I encountered hummocky ice, I met with an
    upset.
I want to laugh. It is not a thing to rejoice over.

Central Eskimo

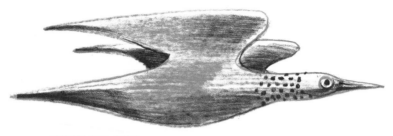

IVORY SEA BIRD

Ayii, ayii, ayii,
My arms, they wave high in the air,
My hands, they flutter behind my back,
They wave above my head
Like the wings of a bird.
Let me move my feet.
Let me dance.
Let me shrug my shoulders.
Let me shake my body.
Let me crouch down.
My arms, let me fold them.
Let me hold my hands under my chin.

Central Eskimo

IVORY WOMAN FLYING

Ayii, Ayii, Ayii,
I wish to see the musk ox run again.
It is not enough for me
To sing of the dear beasts.
Sitting here in the igloo,
My songs fade away,
My words melt away,
Like hills in fog.
Ayii, Ayii, Ayii.

Central Eskimo

That woman down there beneath the sea,
She wants to hide the seals from us.
These hunters in the dance house,
They cannot right matters.
They cannot mend matters.
Into the spirit world
Will go I,
Where no humans dwell.
Set matters right will I.
Set matters right will I.

DRUM DANCER, STONE

Central Eskimo

ANCIENT DORSET ESKIMO
IVORY CARVING WITH NARWHALS

My eyes are tired,
my worn-out eyes,
which never more will follow the narwhal
when shooting up from the deep,
in order to break the waves of the sea,
and my muscles will nevermore tremble
when I seize the harpoon,
ijaja—a—ijaja—aje.

Wish that the souls
of the great sea animals I killed
would help me to get
my heavy thoughts to a distance.
Wish that the memory
of all my great hunts
might lift me out of the weakness of old age,
ijaja—a—ijaja—aje.

Let my breath blow a song
Of all this which calls to mind
my youth.
My song breaks from my throat
with the breath of my life.

Greenland Eskimo

THE MOON,
MODERN ESKIMO
STONE CARVING

I am afraid
When my eyes follow the moon
On its old trail.
I am afraid
When I hear the wind wailing
And the murmuring of snow.
I am afraid
When I watch the stars
Moving on their nightly trail.
I am afraid.

Eastern Eskimo

It is still in the house;
The snowstorm wails outside.
My little boy is sleeping on my back;
His stomach is bulging round.
Is it strange if I start to cry with joy?

Greenland Eskimo

MOTHER AND CHILD,
MODERN ESKIMO STONE CARVING

There is joy in feeling warmth
Come into the world,
To watch the sun retrace its ancient
footprints in the summer sky.

Central Eskimo

IVORY EYE PROTECTORS

Ayii, Ayii,
I think over again my small adventures
When with the wind I drifted in my kayak
And thought I was in danger.
My fears,
Those small ones that seemed so big,
For all the vital things
I had to get and to reach.
And yet there is only one great thing,
The only thing,
To live to see the great day that dawns
And the light that fills the world.

Eastern Eskimo

I arise with movements
swift as a raven's wing,
I arise to meet the day,
My face is turned from the dark of night
To gaze at the new dawn whitening the sky.

Eastern Eskimo

Onto a boy's arm came a mosquito.
"Don't hit! Don't hit!" it hummed,
"Grandchildren have I to sing to."
"Imagine," the boy said,
"So small and yet a grandfather."

Eastern Eskimo

ESKIMO BIRDMAN,
STONE

Ayii, Ayii,
I return to my little song,
And patiently I sing it
Above fishing holes in the ice
Else I too quickly tire
When fishing upstream,
When the wind blows cold,
Where I stand shivering.
Not giving myself time to wait for them
I go home saying
It was the fish that failed—upstream.

Eastern Eskimo

ESKIMO STONE CARVING,
MAN FISHING

Ayii, Ayii, Ayii,
That big man, the one you killed,
the one that led this camp,
He said we should move inland
toward the sun.
That would make others happy.
But not me.
For my soul has gone away
with that man.
Ayii, Ayii, Ayii.

Eastern Eskimo

ESKIMO STONE CARVING,
CARIBOU

Beast of the Sea,
Come and offer yourself in the dear early morning!
Beast of the Plain!
Come and offer yourself in the dear early morning!

Eastern Eskimo

Ayii, Ayii,
The great sea has set me in motion,
Set me adrift,
And I move as a weed in the river.
The arch of sky
And mightiness of storms
Encompasses me,
And I am left
Trembling with joy.

Eastern Eskimo

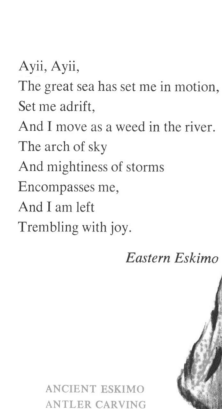

ANCIENT ESKIMO
ANTLER CARVING

When the raven became aware of himself,
light came into the world,
and grass tussocks turned into men.

Eastern Eskimo

MODERN ESKIMO RAVEN CARVING

Ayii, Ayii,
I walked on the ice of the sea.
Wondering, I heard
The song of the sea
And the great sighing
Of new formed ice.
Go then go!
Strength of soul
Brings health
To the place of feasting.

Eastern Eskimo

WHALEBONE WALKING MAN

Ayii, Ayii, Ayii,
I am good looking.
My face is beautiful.
I have long shining hair.
My lips and cheeks are red.
And my nose between the eyes
is flat and well formed.
Ayii, Ayii.

Eastern Eskimo

ANCIENT IVORY FEMALE FIGURE

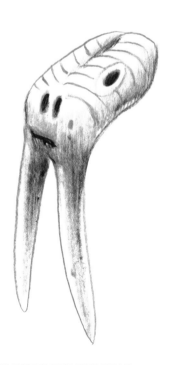

ANCIENT IVORY WALRUS HEAD

MODERN ESKIMO
STONE FIGURE,
SEA GOD

Who will, who will,
play this game,
play this game,
jump in the air,
jump in the air,
tremble in the knees,
jump in the air,
blow up in the air?
Ayii, Ayii.

   Eastern Eskimo

Acknowledgments

The editor acknowledges with gratitude the assistance of his Indian friends, Nelson Hales and Natawapio, and the assistance of his Eskimo friends, Pootoogook, Pitseolak, Oshaweetok, Tigoodligak, Kingwachiak, and Ikhaluk.

He also wishes to acknowledge as source material the following books, periodicals, and publications: translations from the original Indian and Eskimo dialects by Franz Boas, Daniel G. Brinton, Frances Densmore, Alice Cunningham Fletcher, Walter James Hoffman, Francis LaFlesche, Washington Matthews, James Mooney, Frank Russell, Matilda Coxe Stevenson, from *Annual Report, Bulletin,* Bureau of American Ethnology, 1887-1939/"The Sun Dance and Other Ceremonies of the Teton Dakota" by J. R. Walker, 1917 (Vol. 16, Part II); "Havasupai Ethnography" by Leslie Spier, 1928 (Vol. 29, Part III); "Navaho Texts" by Pliny Earle Goddard, 1933 (Vol. 34, Part I), from *Anthropological Papers,* American Museum of Natural History/*American Indian Design and Decoration* by LeRoy H. Appleton, Dover Pictorial Archive Series, Dover Publications, Inc., 1971/*The American Rhythm* by Mary Austin, Harcourt, Brace and Company, 1923, and Cooper Square, 1971/*Indian Days on the Western Prairies* by Marius Barbeau, Queen's Printer, Ottawa, 1960 (by permission of Information Canada)/"Myths and Legends of the New York State Iroquois" by Harriett Maxwell Converse, from *New York State Museum Bulletin 125,* December, 1908/*Creation Myths of Primitive America* by Jeremiah Curtin, Little, Brown and Company, 1898/*The Indians' Book* by Natalie Curtis (Burlin), Harper & Brothers, 1907, and Dover Publications, Inc., 1968/*Lamba Folklore* by Clement M. Doke, American Folklore Society, 1929/*Canadian Eskimo Art* by James Houston, Queen's Printer, Ottawa, 1932 (by permission of Information Canada)/*The White Dawn* by James Houston, Harcourt Brace Jovanovich, Inc., 1971/*Canadian Arctic Expedition, 1913-18* by Jenness Diamond, Queen's Printer, Ottawa, 1923 (by permission of Information Canada)/*Indians of Canada* by Jenness Diamond, Queen's Printer, Ottawa, 1932 (by permission of Information Canada)/*Intellectual Culture of the Iglulik Eskimos,* Vol. 7, 1929, *The Netsilik Eskimos: Social Life and Spiritual Culture,* Vol. 8, 1931, *Intellectual Culture of the Copper Eskimos,* Vol. 9, 1932, from *Report of the Fifth Thule Expedition* by Knud Rasmussen/"Aboriginal American Poetry" by John Reade, from *Transactions,* Royal Society of Canada, 1887/*Songs of the Tewa* by Herbert Joseph Spinden, Exposition of the Indian Tribal Arts, 1933/"Haida Songs" by John Swanton, from *Publications,* Vol. 3, American Ethnological Society, 1912/*Singing For Power: The Song Magic of the Papago Indians of Southern Arizona* by Ruth Underhill, University of California Press, 1938, 1969.